My Very First Hide and Seek Things that Go

Let's search for things that go!

It's **noisy** on the **city** street.
The trucks go **honk**
and the cars go **beep**!

Look around. Can you find . . .

a green car

2 yellow cars

a bicycle

a limousine

a garbage truck

a school bus

a tanker

3 motorcycles

a truck

a car transporter

an underground train

a train

a van

Can you find a cat
in a basket?

How many yellow vehicles can you count?

Look for a very long car!

The **sirens** blare.
The **lights** flash bright.
Ready to **help**, all **day** and **night**!

Look around. Can you find . . .

a police
van

5 police
cars

4 fire
trucks

4 police
motorcycles

a police
helicopter

an ambulance

a firefighter

a firefighter
with a hose

a firefighter
with a ladder

5 police
horses

2 police
officers

3 paramedics

Can you see a police
officer chasing a
fast red car?

Who is rescuing a cat?

What noise does a fire truck make?

Flying smoothly in the **air**, we **take** people everywhere!

Look around. Can you find . . .

 an airship

 a jet

 2 helicopters

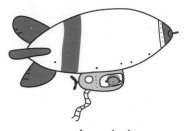 3 hang gliders

 2 light aircrafts

 a spaceship

 3 hot-air balloons

 a glider

 4 parachutes

 2 rockets

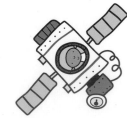 a space station

Can you count the red balloons?

Who else can you see in space?

Which aircraft could fly you to the Moon?

The **builders** carry heavy **loads**
to **build** our homes
and **make** new roads.

Look around. Can you find . . .

a crane

2 excavators

2 rollers

2 bulldozers

5 mixers

3 dump trucks

a cement truck

2 piles of
big blocks

a pile of
bricks

the foreman

5 barriers

6 signs

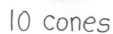
10 cones

What can flatten
bumpy ground?

With quick **engines**
or **sails** unfurled,
we **travel** all around the **world**!

Look around. Can you find . . .

a yacht

a fishing boat

a canoe

2 green sails

3 red sails

a submarine

a cruise ship

4 dinghies

a cargo ship

a tall ship

3 tugboats

a surfer

a speedboat

2 windsurfers

a water-skier

3 rowboats

Who is swimming underwater?

How many beach balls
can you count?

Which giant boat
has white sails?

My Very First Hide and Seek Things that Go

Let's search for things that go!
Have fun exploring this big, busy book,
packed full of amazing vehicles to find.

Illustrated by John A. Abbott

Castle Street Press
The Wilderness, Berkhamsted, Hertfordshire, HP4 2AZ, UK.
501 Nelson Place, P.O. Box 141000, Nashville, TN 37214-1000, USA.

We manufacture with paper
from sustainable forests.

We check our suppliers'
working conditions.

We believe in recycling waste
and saving energy.

www.makebelieveideas.com

We Care

Parental Guidance

Read together

Helps teach
first words

0+ YEARS

£6.99 U.K. $9.99 U.S. / CAN

ISBN10: 1-78393-637-1
ISBN13: 978-1-78393-637-3

9 781783 936373

12201401

T2-FCV-936